Home sweet home

One of these animals doesn't live in the forest. Do you know which? Do you know the names of all the animals? Find the stickers to fill the spaces.

1

2

3

4

5

6

7

8

Forest fact

The stag deer is the most majestic animal in the forest. It is e... It shed... and gr... every yea...

D1275219

The swan (6) doesn't live in the forest. The others are: 1 moose 2 owl 3 snake 4 chipmunk 5 squirrel 7 rabbits 8 deer

Hunger game
Which of the coloured paths will lead the hare to the carrots?

Family fun
Which animal belongs to a different group from the others?

1

2

4

3

5

7

6

The red path leads to the carrots. All of the animals are mammals except for 3, the snake, which is a reptile.

Over to you

Finish drawing the badger by joining the dots
to look like the framed picture.

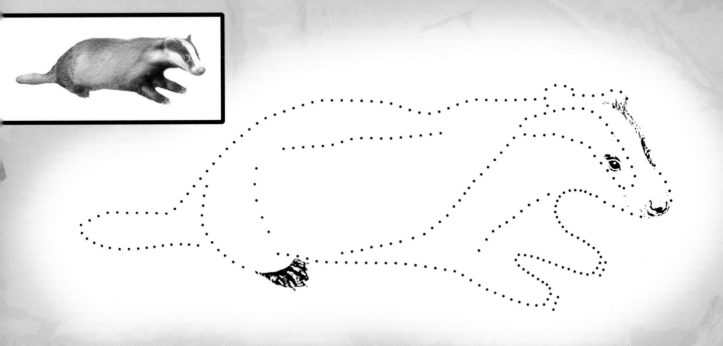

Forest fact

The main food of a giant
panda is bamboo, but
it does sometimes eat
other grasses and roots.
It will even eat eggs
and small animals and
birds. It munches almost
constantly and poos up
to 40 times a day!

Forest fact

The genet is a small African mammal that hunts for rodents and other small creatures. It has sharp claws to help it climb easily up tree trunks.

Run away!

Draw a path to help the mouse get to the seeds, scampering past the birds of prey.

No place like home
Some of these birds don't live in the forest.
Do you know what they are and where they live?

1

2

3

4

6

5

7

8

Look for the stickers!

Number 5 is a puffin and 8 is a tern. They both live on the coast. Number 3 is a kingfisher which lives near water.

START

How to play
Find a playing piece for each player. Take it in turns to throw a dice and move along the path.

Look for the stickers!

Snake! Go back 2 spaces.

Butterfly! Move forward 3 spaces.

Look at me!
Hedgehogs are very common in European woods and forests. They are not very big (up to 30cm), but use their prickly spines to defend themselves. Make sure you watch for them on the roads as they often get run over.

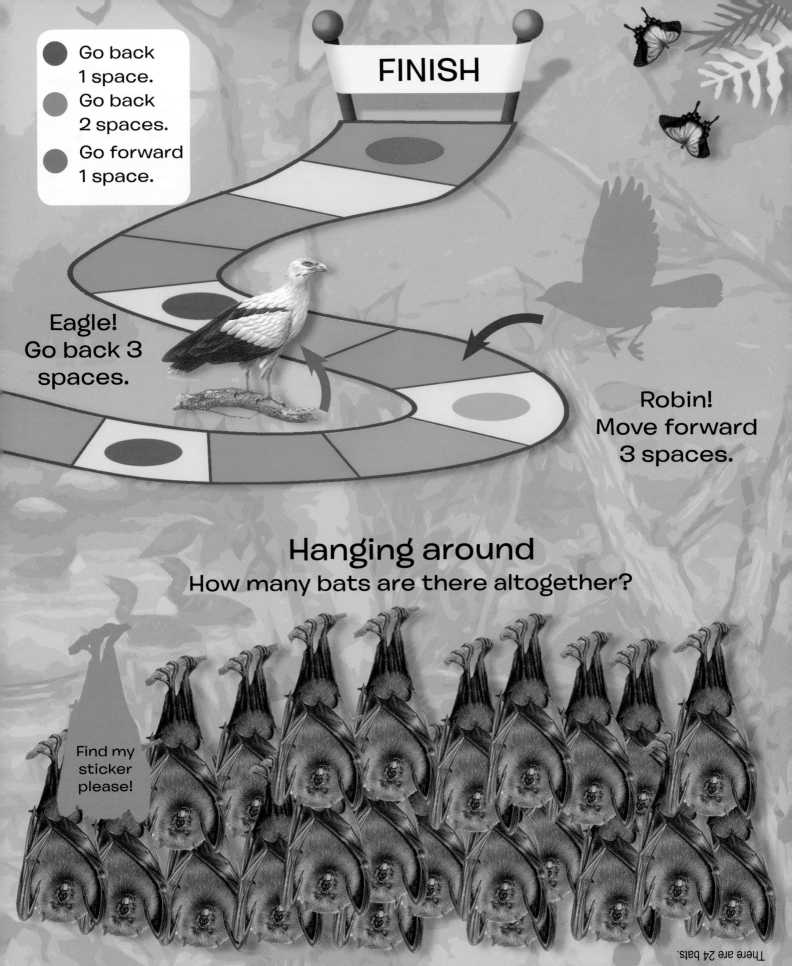

- Go back 1 space.
- Go back 2 spaces.
- Go forward 1 space.

FINISH

Eagle! Go back 3 spaces.

Robin! Move forward 3 spaces.

Hanging around
How many bats are there altogether?

Find my sticker please!

There are 24 bats.

Forest fact

The red panda is not related to the giant panda. It is much smaller, too: about the size of a pet cat. They do eat bamboo, but also love fruits and eggs.

Odd one out

Turkeys live in the forests of Mexico and the USA. One of these is slightly different. Can you see which one?

1

2

3

4

Turkey 2 has a yellow head.

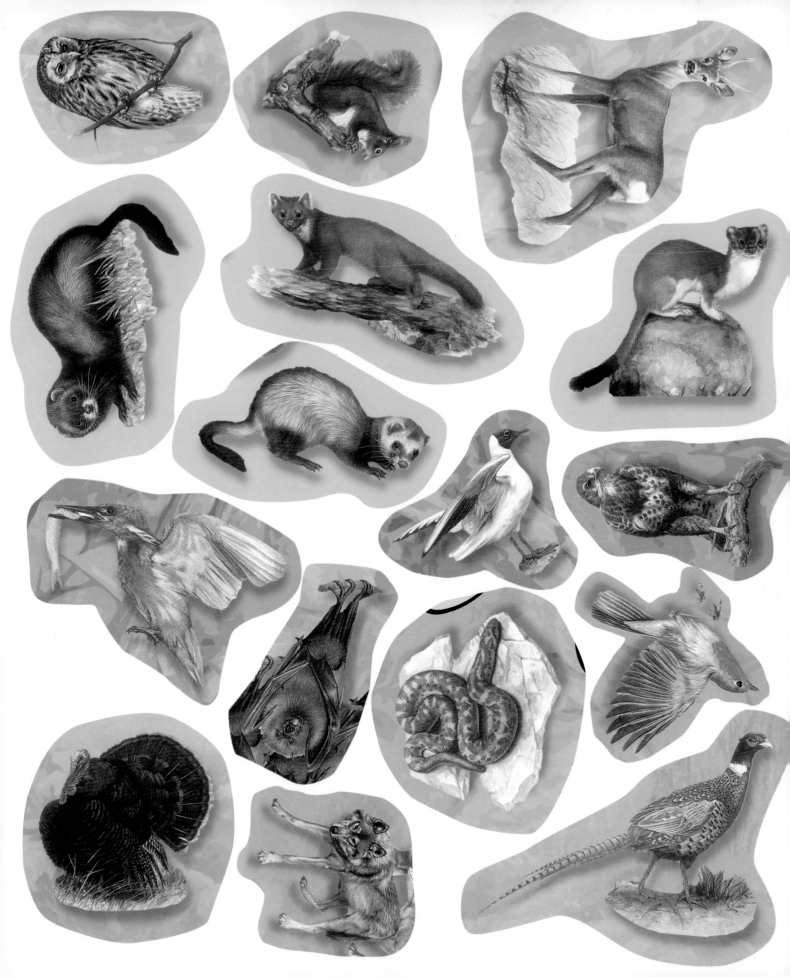

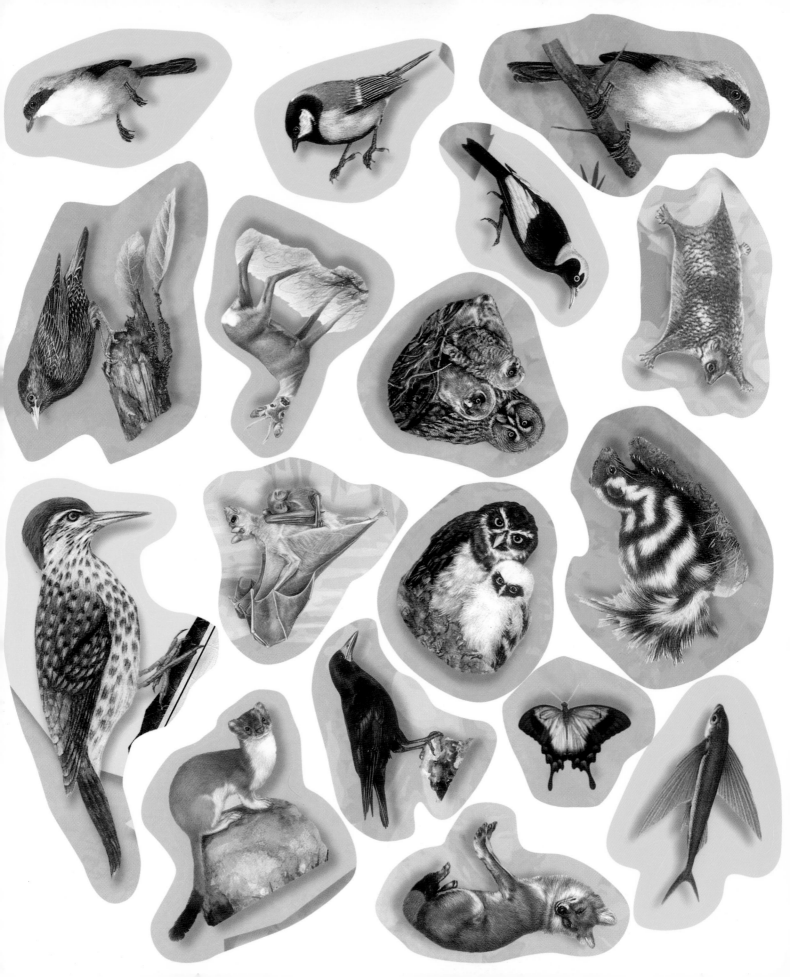

Forest trail

Which path will lead the pheasant to the worm?

Look for the
stickers!

Copy and colour

Copy the picture, square by square, to draw the bear.

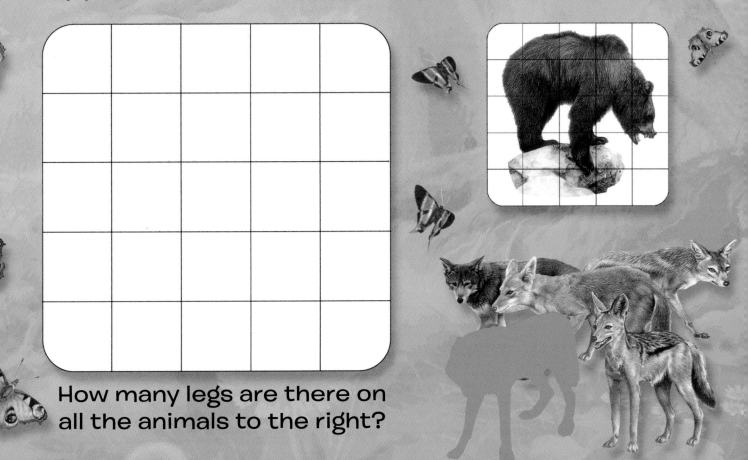

How many legs are there on
all the animals to the right?

Forest fact

The red fox hunts at night, catching birds, rabbits and rodents. It loves chickens, so take care if you keep them in your garden!

In the air

Stick the stickers on the page, and then find which of the flying creatures is not a bird.

1

2

3

4

5

6

7

8

Finish the fox

Join the dots, and then colour the rest of the fur to match.

Which way?

Trace a path through the trees to take the bird to its snack.

Find my sticker please!

Who's whoooo?

Find the stickers to fill the gaps, and then work out which of the birds doesn't belong to the owl family.

1

2

3

4

5

6

7

Too many pieces

Which of the pieces doesn't come from the main picture?

1

2

3

4

5

6

7

8

9

10

Bird 6 is not an owl. Piece 5 is not from the picture.

Food maze
Help this woodpecker through the maze to get to the worm on the other side.

Maze answer:

Look for the stickers!

Spotted!
Look for three differences between the spotted skunks.

Find my sticker please!

The tail on the righthand one is bigger, and it has a red nose and no spot on its forehead.

Look for the stickers!

Memory game
Stick the stickers, remember the pictures, and then turn the page.

Going batty
All of these creatures fly, but they aren't all bats.
Do you know which one is not?

1

2

3

4

5

6

Number 5 is a flying squirrel.

Forest fact

The wild cat looks similar to a pet cat. However, it has a bigger, stronger body and a bushier tail. Some have striped fur but other types are spotted.

Who's hiding?
Some animals are hiding in the plants.
Do you know what they are?

1

2

3

4

5

Can you remember?

Think back to the animals on the previous page. There is an extra one here. Can you see it?

Look for the stickers!

Forest fact

Wild boars can't see very well, but they have an excellent sense of smell. They can sniff out food from over 100 metres away!

The new animal is the eagle.

Animal World Stickers
In the Forest

Collect the other titles in this series

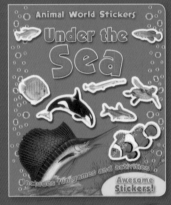

Animal World Stickers
Under the Sea
Includes fun games and activities
Awesome Stickers!

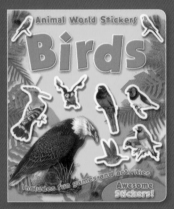

Animal World Stickers
Birds
Includes fun games and activities
Awesome Stickers!

Animal World Stickers
In the Forest
Includes fun games and activities
Awesome Stickers!

Animal World Stickers
In the Jungle
Includes fun games and activities
Awesome Stickers!

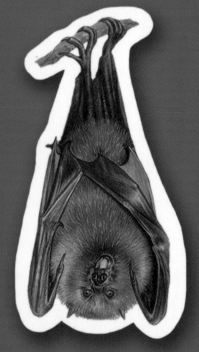

Brown Watson

ENGLAND LE8 0HG

Printed in Malaysia

AST5-8

© 2016 Brown Watson, English Edition

© Todolibro Ediciones, S.A.

£2.50

ISBN 978-0-7097-2324-0

9 780709 723240

T2-CVQ-556

A collection of figures, diagrams, and art

that illustrate key concepts in your text.

Each figure appears on its own page so

you can take notes during lectures.

TAKE NOTE!

To ACCOMPANY

PSYCHOLOGY
Mind, Brain, and Culture
Second Edition

Drew Westen

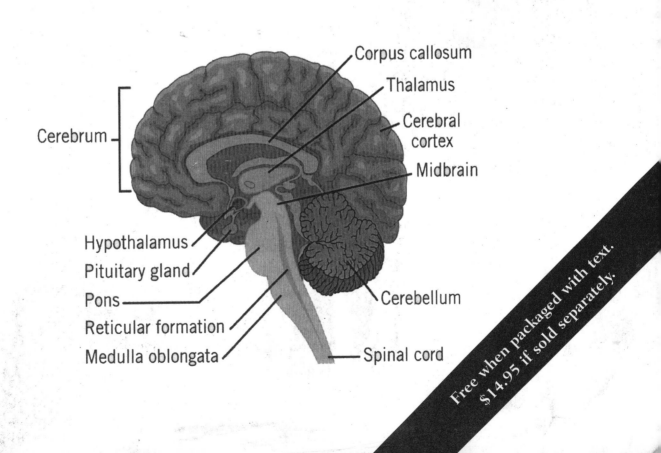

- Corpus callosum
- Thalamus
- Cerebral cortex
- Midbrain
- Cerebrum
- Hypothalamus
- Pituitary gland
- Pons
- Reticular formation
- Medulla oblongata
- Cerebellum
- Spinal cord